Your Child and Mathematics

by W H Cockcroft

A short survey of the aims and methods of modern mathematics teaching of five- to thirteen-year-old children, written particularly for parents, in association with the Nuffield Mathematics Project.

W & R Chambers and John Murray

Library edition:
550 20231 5 (Chambers)
7195 1812 1 (Murray)

Paperback edition:
550 20230 7 (Chambers)
7195 1809 1 (Murray)

Manresa House.

First published May 1968
Second impression October 1968

Printed in Great Britain by
Newgate Press Limited
London EC1

Introduction

Have you a son, a daughter, a niece, a nephew, or a grandchild at school and under the age of thirteen? Even if you have no younger relations at school, do you have a general interest in the education of younger children?

If you can say **yes** to either of these questions, then you have probably also noticed that great changes in teaching methods have been taking place in primary and junior or 'middle' schools* in recent years. Classes have often been too large for comfort. Physical circumstances have often imposed intolerably difficult problems. Nevertheless, a dedicated band of teachers, mainly women, have fought to change our approach to the teaching of younger children. Their aim, and the aim of those who have supported them, has been to base the education of five- to thirteen-year-olds on class activity in which the children can join, learning from their own experience, **understanding by doing.** The changes involved in this newer approach are revolutionary when viewed in terms of the older one in which children were expected to accept passively facts and processes imposed upon them, often irrespective of whether their natural interest had been roused or a measure of real understanding obtained.

You will certainly see some of the progress which has been made if there is a newly built or extended primary school in your neighbourhood. In such a school you will not find orderly rows of desks, but rooms in which children can join together in convenient groups, rooms with walls on which individual and joint work can be displayed, and alcoves in which various sectional interests can be pursued. This is how architects and designers have responded to the needs of the modern teacher and our children. They have tried to create schools in which the teacher will no longer expect children to memorise facts for their own sake, or to learn by rote. Instead the teacher will find it natural to join the children in an exploration of the world around them, an exploration in which the children may be as much the leaders as the teacher.

There are many variations in the names of schools for five- to nine-year-old children and for nine- to thirteen-year-olds. To avoid confusion the terms 'primary' to denote schools for five- to nine-year-olds and 'middle' (i.e. between primary and secondary proper) for schools for nine- to thirteen-year-olds will be used throughout.

In mathematics, the differences between the old and the new methods are most marked. Trickery and technique alone cannot be accepted. The subject must not be taught as a series of rules, without reasons. Its aim is not a series of right answers to a long series of sums, in which the methods have usually been memorised without the necessary understanding having first been obtained. Do you remember rules like **turn it upside down and multiply**? If you do, you may also remember having wanted at some time or other to ask the very reasonable question 'Why?', and being dissatisfied with the possible answer 'Because it works'. Without more discussion of this question you might well never understand division by fractions, and sums involving this process could deteriorate into a meaningless mumbo-jumbo. This lack of real understanding made mathematics difficult and often unacceptable to many of us.

Worse still, many of us with an apparent competence in mechanical arithmetic found ourselves unable to do problems. Signs and symbols introduced too early, tricks and techniques learned by rote, lack of understanding of the need to build up an adequate vocabulary and a comprehension of written and spoken English, all added to the difficulties experienced by so many of us. We were confined to **equalities** such as $4 + 5 = 9$ or $10 - 5 = 5$, with hardly a reference to **unequal** things, although in practice inequalities are more usual than equalities; a child needs to understand that 5 is **greater** than 4, and 7 is **less** than 8, etc., if he is to grasp what equality really means, especially in such forms as $4 + 1 = 3 + 2$. We were rarely given the opportunity to explore and make precise the physical ideas underlying the so-called practical use of our early mathematics; a child using a word such as **bigger** may mean **longer, wider, taller** or **fatter** according to his experience and his ability to express himself more or less precisely. To understand these and other mathematical ideas young children need a variety of practical experience and an opportunity for discussion — both with a teacher and among themselves — about these experiences.

The classroom of today's primary and middle school child is thus full of equipment and associated projects of all kinds. Children work together, and with a teacher, using 'rods', 'blocks', number strips, abaci, coloured sticky paper, sand, water, pots, jars and containers of all kinds, nail-boards and rubber bands, to mention but a few of the practical everyday materials now considered part of the equipment of almost every primary school classroom. Learning by doing, instead of by memory alone, is the order of the day.

The Nuffield Mathematics Project is based on the work of pioneering teachers who for many years have been laying the foundation for this modern approach. Its aim is to produce a contemporary course in mathematics for children aged from five to thirteen. It is drawing together the 'best of the old' and the 'best of the new' and is firmly linked with the practical experience of present-day teachers in our schools. Preliminary Guides have been distributed in chosen areas throughout the country. These have been revised in the light of comment and criticism from teachers who have used the material in their own classrooms. Only after this revision have the Teachers' Guides gone to press and become generally available. The cooperation of the Department of Education and Science and of Local Education Authorities has ensured that the influence of the work has spread widely. Centres, in which teachers can exchange views and ideas about their work, have been set up by Local Education Authorities in many parts of the country. These have become meeting points for teachers at all levels and in all subjects. Work at primary and middle level cannot stand alone; it must match with work taking place in developing new secondary school curricula. Work in mathematics must also be linked in attitude with work in other subjects at its own level if it is ultimately to be successful in arousing and maintaining the interest and enthusiasm of all our school children and teachers. The Nuffield Guides for teachers have been written with all this in mind. It is hoped that they will attract the interest of anyone concerned with children. They contain a wealth of children's work, impressive in its enthusiasm and gaiety, and going even further than it was dared to hope in demonstrating the skill, interest and understanding which our children can achieve.

My aim in what follows is to describe some of the main lines of the Nuffield work and to invite your cooperation and interest in the Project. I hope that I can tell you enough about the primary and middle school work to help you to understand modern methods and appreciate the attitude adopted by the Nuffield Mathematics Project. If your reaction is one of resignation, if you are saying that you were never any good at mathematics at school, my invitation to read on is a most warm one. Only a fool would claim to turn geese into swans, or make light of what can be hard work. But teachers in the Project do claim (and can produce ample evidence to justify their claim) that lack of interest and a feeling of complete hopelessness in the subject can be eradicated. A statement such as 'I never could do sums and hated mathematics', can be replaced by 'I often made mistakes in mathematics, but at least I saw the point of it all and quite liked the things we did'. Whether we like it or not, our children will be concerned in the future with more 'abstract' mathematics than were their predecessors. The world of computers and computer programmes, of automatic production-line processes, or of operational research by managements, is a far cry from the world of the nineteenth-century clerk, mill-hand or small industrialist. Our most important task must be to teach children to think mathematically for themselves. From a gradual awareness of the patterns of ideas lying behind their practical experiences, there must be built up a willingness to accept the underlying mathematical ways of thinking which are proving so vital in the development of modern technological society.

A page from a book on 'Shapes and how we use them' made by some six- and seven-year-old children in an infants' school.

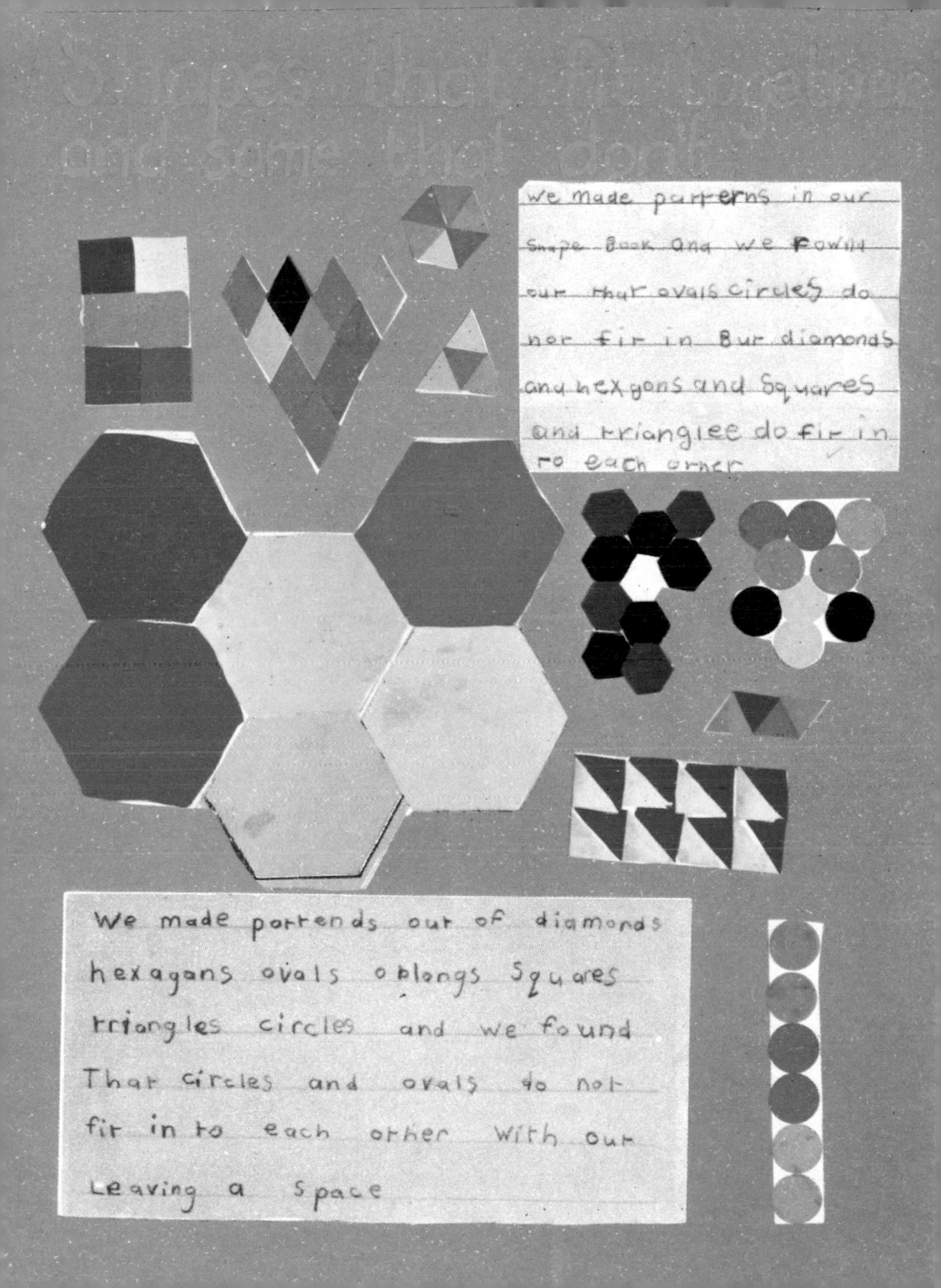

Shapes that fit together and some that don't
we made patterns in our
Shape Book and we fownd
out that ovals circles do
not fit in But diamonds
and hexgons and Squares
and trianglee do fit in
to each other
We made pattends out of diamonds
hexagans ovals oblongs Squares
triangles circles and we found
That circles and ovals do not
fit in to each other with out
Leaving a space

Beginnings
Primary work: five to nine years old

Most of us have a picture in our mind's eye of a primary school teacher as a person in front of a class of small children, sitting at a high desk, or standing at a blackboard, with all the required knowledge in her mind, ready to deal it out as necessary, in larger or smaller portions, to the children under her authority. Thinking of primary level teaching in this way, one may almost be tempted to draw a parallel with the much quoted description by St. John: 'In the beginning was the Word, and the Word was with God, and the Word was God' (John. i. 1). Any teacher must certainly have the 'Word', but in pursuing this parallel with St. John's description it is particularly relevant to remember that in the Greek version of the New Testament this quotation implies that in the beginning there was **reason**, or **rationality,** and these were with God.

In fact, of course, school teachers need both knowledge of what they wish to teach, and an understanding of those who are to be taught. Relative to her class, the primary school teacher in particular may well appear almost God-like in her knowledge and understanding of things. But however knowledgeable she may be about factual matters, she can only communicate successfully with a class as a whole when she knows the children are all capable of understanding what she has to offer.

In the beginning, with our youngest school children, this raises problems which must be overcome before serious teaching can start. There can be no 'streams' of dull and bright children at the start of primary education. The teacher must communicate as successfully as possible with **all** the children. First, therefore, the teacher of beginners must get to know her children, and get to know them well. She cannot assume they have all begun school with the same experiences, and reactions to those experiences, behind them. There are no previous school records the teacher can consult. Before she can introduce her class to even simple mathematical ideas she must find out something of what they have each done at home, what has interested them, and what they have understood about the world around them. The child who has ridden a tricycle may intuitively know something about wheels and turning, from practical experience, which a child who has not ridden a tricycle cannot know. One child playing in a sandpit with a bucket and spade may have grasped more of the idea of **too much** or **too little,** or of **amount of space to be filled,** than another child. One child may have picked up an above-average range of vocabulary so that he already understands how to use words such as **wide, fat, high, tall** or **long,** in relation to **big** ; another may not.

Best of all, a child may have been lucky enough to have lived with articulate and understanding adults, able and willing to join with him in the enjoyment of seeing, hearing and learning to know the world in which he lives. Heaven forbid, however, that contact of children with parents or adults in general should therefore be thought of as a deliberate teaching process. The simple genuine interest of a parent or a friend in a child's activity will widen the value of that activity. It is on precisely this principle that our most successful nursery 'schools' are organised. The games children play, the toys they have, the many things they have had to do at home before coming to school, are the basis on which a teacher has to build in the beginning. The children who go to school with the greatest advantage are those whose natural interest in the world has been strengthened by contact with understanding adults, and who have at the same time gained an ease, fluency and flexibility in their use of language. All the skill and experience of a teacher of beginners is needed to widen the horizons and deepen the experience of those children in her class who have not had these advantages.

Once the primary teacher has overcome the difficulties involved in this first stage with beginners, she can start to move towards the study of mathematical ideas. There are now recognised to be three main lines to be followed in the formation of basic mathematical concepts by children in primary school before they enter middle school at about the age of nine. First, as one would imagine, there is **number work,** ranging from simple counting to an understanding of the arithmetical operations of addition and multiplication. Secondly, in parallel with work on number, the child must develop a sufficient understanding of the physical properties of solids and liquids so as to make sense of such 'three-dimensional' mathematical ideas as those of **weight** and **volume.** Similarly 'in two dimensions' children must come to understand what **length** and **area** mean. Finally, together with all this 'environmental' work, there must be a third line of development in which more purely geometrical concepts must be recognised and understood. Children are not born with an understanding of **straight lines, angles, verticality, horizontality,** or of **perspective**. Until they have grasped these concepts, they cannot be expected to appreciate and understand the geometrical frame which the adult imposes on the world.

Of course, these three lines of development cannot be mathematically separated. **Numbers** occur throughout work on **measurement; straight lines** occur in practice both before and after they occur in an 'imaginary' fashion from one point in 'space' to another; **corners** are recognised before **angular measurement** is understood, but afterwards they can be 'measured'. Experience leads to abstraction, but once abstraction has taken place, it influences our reactions to our experiences and imposes a pattern on them.

The three lines are also inseparable since in each of them hand, eye and thought all have a part to play. Beyond them, moving on from the understanding of concrete operations as they occur in practice, one must work towards an understanding of the more abstract and theoretical operations of middle school mathematics. This is not to say that at the earlier levels abstract theoretical work is useless or impossible; nor, at the later levels, that one does not gain a better understanding by working in concrete, practical terms. Those in the Nuffield Project believe, on the one hand, that at all levels there must be a recognition of the theoretical, abstract, mathematical patterns of thought behind apparently dissimilar situations. On the other hand, they also believe that a far greater understanding of theoretical and abstract processes in mathematics is obtained by working experimentally in concrete situations.

Consider the idea of 'number' from this point of view. Long before they come to school for the first time, children will show an ability to sort things – putting them into categories. It may be **cars** as opposed to **bicycles**, or **Minis** as opposed to **Jaguars**, or **red** cars and **blue** cars, **my** toys and **your** toys, things which are **upstairs** and things which are **downstairs**, and so on; whatever the particular situation, to be able to sort things in this way implies some understanding of relationships between things – how they can be sorted according to relationships, and how

things dissimilar in one respect can be matched in another. The teacher must guide the child so that this ability is refined: it is one thing to be able to recognise **redness** so as to be able to understand the similarity of **red** cars and **red** pencils in this respect, but another thing to be able to recognise **fiveness** in **five cars** as opposed to **four bicycles**. This is the first stage of mathematical abstraction; until it is passed there is no point in attempting to proceed further with a child in his number work. The necessary refinement of a child's ability can only be done by guidance through 'experiments' in which collections of things are studied in various practical situations, until when appropriate the child recognises the 'fiveness' of a collection of five things.

By exploring the child's understanding of his experience with collections of things, a teacher can give the right guidance to help the child make the appropriate interpretations and abstractions. If necessary at any stage the teacher must be willing to let the child move back half a step so as to move forward a full step at a later stage. Once the child can on request give the teacher five pencils or five marbles, say, and clearly cannot understand that there could ever have been any doubt about the matter, the game has been won.

Having abstracted the first idea of **number** from varied experiences with collections of things, the child can move on to understand how numbers are related to one another. Here the first aim is the study of the numbers 1, 2, 3, . . ., in sequence. Once again experience, observation and theoretical interpretation are all needed. Checks of the understanding attained will again be possible and will be part of the guidance provided by the teacher. Awareness of the idea that one number may be **greater than** another and that numbers can be ordered by this relationship is abstracted from many experiences. Houses which are next to one another in a row, boxes which nest within one another, buttons or coins of graduated size, the various rungs of a ladder, collections of things and the smaller collections of things which they contain, are all examples of such experiences. They all lead to an acceptance of a **number strip** – a piece of wood or thick card marked off, in the first instance, from one to ten.

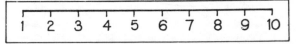

Next the child can consider how numbers are related by the operation of **addition**. Once again we use suitable experience with collections of things. Addition is an abstraction of all the situations in which we put together distinct collections. The gap to be bridged is typified by the two extreme statements:

(i) I had 3 conkers. Jane gave me 2 more, so now I have 5.

(ii) $3 + 2 = 5$.

Easily constructed experiments lead to pictorial representations illustrating additive relationships in a variety of ways:

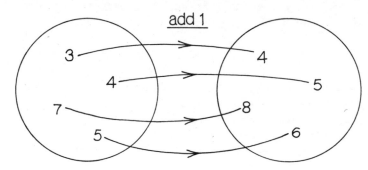

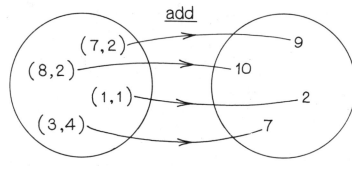

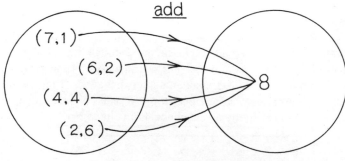

Children will readily draw such pictures to illustrate their practical observations. The Nuffield Guides recommend that advantage should be taken of this whenever possible. Such child-produced illustrations provide a link between the practical and the theoretical, whose value has not been fully recognised in the past. When they are classifying collections of things at the earliest stage, children should be introduced to illustrations of the following kind:

From such illustrations they can be easily led to approve of records of the form:

	scent	no scent	smooth stem	hairy stem
primrose	×			×
violet	×		×	
bluebell	×		×	
wood anemone		×		×
celandine		×	×	
lords and ladies		×	×	

Given the opportunity, children will soon go even further and produce 'graphs' of the form overleaf: of class absences, of team points, of tickets sold each day before the school concert, of the number of children from each district around the school, and so on.

Exploring 'clock' arithmetic can deepen understanding of the ordinary one and of arithmetical processes.

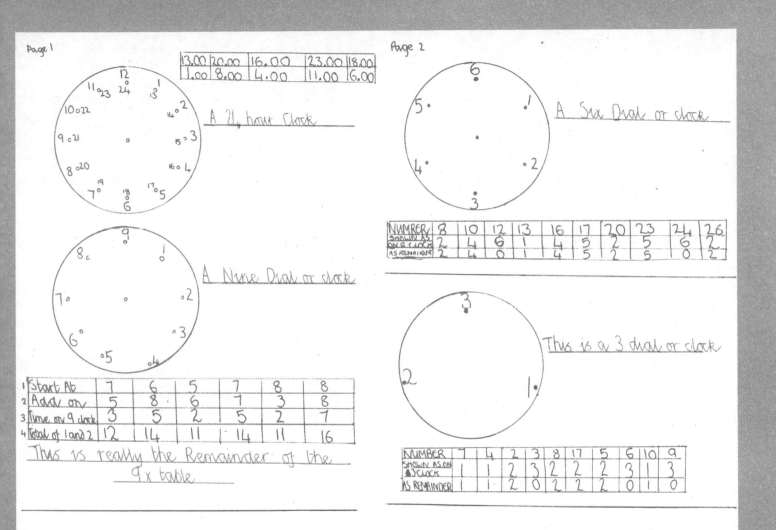

Page 1:

13.00	20.00	16.00	23.00	18.00
1.00	8.00	4.00	11.00	6.00

A 24 hour clock

A Nine Dial or clock

1 Start At	7	6	5	7	8	8
2 Add on	5	8	6	7	3	8
3 Time on 9 clock	3	5	2	5	2	7
4 Total of 1 and 2	12	14	11	14	11	16

This is really the Remainder of the
9 x table

Page 2:

A Six Dial or clock

NUMBER	8	10	12	13	16	17	20	23	24	26
SHOWN AS ON 6 CLOCK	2	4	6	1	4	5	2	5	6	2
AS REMAINDER	2	4	0	1	4	5	2	5	0	2

This is a 3 dial or clock

NUMBER	7	4	2	3	8	17	5	6	10	9
SHOWN AS ON 3 CLOCK	1	1	2	3	2	2	2	3	1	3
AS REMAINDER	1	1	2	0	2	2	2	0	1	0

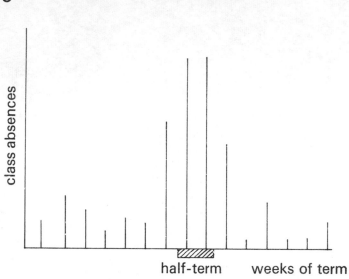

half-term   weeks of term

Thus from the earliest age children can be led to understand that the pictorial representation of mathematical information enhances the value of that information. Quite apart from its purely educational value this is a lesson well worth learning if one is to see the point of modern methods of presenting statistical information in the press and on television.

Pictorial representation of this kind should rightly be regarded at first as child-made apparatus leading to a better understanding of the processes of elementary mathematics. While producing such representations, children can also work with the various kinds of manufactured 'rods' and 'blocks' now commonly used in schools. Such apparatus lends to arithmetic a reality missing from the older, purely 'bookwork', approach and many parents will have observed how its use in the classroom has affected their children's early arithmetic. First steps in addition and multiplication are certainly made more understandable for many children when such apparatus is used. The concrete relationships between the different shapes involved give another example of how mathematical ideas can be illustrated, and more readily grasped and understood, by physical experience and 'seeing for oneself'.

In the past we have tended to teach the elementary ideas of arithmetic 'abstractly' too early in the child's development, before true understanding can be expected. Now, for example, we see addition as a process to be developed quite slowly and thoroughly

out of operations with collections of things. Pictorial representation and practical work using rods or blocks of suitably related lengths and colours, as necessary, is then a second stage. Excessive paper and pencil work on lots and lots of 'addition sums', say, **done for their own sake** is no longer considered necessary after reasonable familiarity with number relationships has been gained. Doing such work most often only confirmed one in the belief that one could usually expect to get most sums right or most wrong. Further practice can be obtained by paper and pencil work done in connection with practical work in other developments in the subject.

In a similar fashion multiplication can start more thoroughly in terms of practical processes, typified by a situation in which there are two sweets for each of three children, i.e. six sweets in all. After sufficient experience at this level children can begin to work with suitable manufactured apparatus. Once again a large amount of paper work **for its own sake** is not recommended.

We no longer move too quickly from addition and multiplication to subtraction and division. In the past, these processes have been introduced too early, and techniques and tricks have all too often been thought to offer the right approach. One may teach a child to subtract 39 from 47:

$$\begin{array}{r} 47 \\ 39 \\ \hline 8 \end{array}$$

by learning a drill which has as its aim an automatic response: '9 from 7, I can't; borrow one; 9 from 17 equals 8, pay back one; 4 from 4, nothing'. But how does such a drill help one to **understand** the process of subtraction? Why not, for example, let the child carefully learn to understand the basic facts involved in subtraction by moving and counting from one number to another on the number strip?

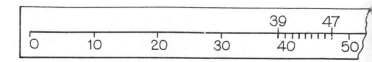

At a later stage, when operations with negative numbers are dealt with in middle school, children may have to evaluate + 17 − (− 9). This is also subtraction. The numbers used here, however, are **directed**: they are either **positive** or **negative** and the number strip has been extended:

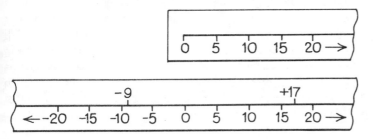

But subtraction is still a process involving moving and counting from one number to another. One has to learn where to find the number −9, so as to recognise that '−9 from +17' involves a 'count' of 9 + 17 = 26, from −9 to +17.

Thus a 'moving and counting' process can equally well be used at primary and middle school level in subtraction. A child who has played with a number strip will accept and understand the idea of moving backwards or forwards on it. Given time and enough practical experience, children can really understand subtraction in these terms. They can then be allowed freedom in their choice of technical method. Moreover, if they start correctly at primary level they will not have to learn a different technique when they later extend their number strip using positive **and** negative numbers. The process of moving and counting on their number lines will extend naturally through a recognition that the direction of the counting is now to be taken into account. Time spent at the earliest stage in developing real understanding is time well spent when the insight gained helps one to accept other ideas later.

In the second line of work at primary level the need for a mixture of experiment and theory is perhaps more obvious. Here, children must develop an understanding of such physical ideas as those of **weight** and **volume**. We link these ideas with those of **length**, **area**, **'shape and size'**, and group all the work together in the beginning, calling it 'environmental mathematics'.

We start with **creative** activity with sand, water, jars, scissors, paper, etc. This can develop into simple constructional work or the sewing and knitting of simple patterns. Music and movement can also play their part in illustrating patterns of rhythm in sound and geometrical patterns of movement in simple games and dances for young children. **Imitative** activity, adding an air of reality to environmental work, is easily evolved by play in 'shops' and in simple 'cookery'. A point to note is that in such practical activity there are not only skills to be learned for use in later life, but also purely mathematical lessons to be learned. Shopping involves learning in practice to understand the ideas underlying the use of words such as **less than, greater than, lighter than, heavier than, longer than,** and **shorter than.** Cooking buns can involve the **cost of materials** and the implied cost of each of twelve buns made; 'quantities' are certainly needed, as may be a measurement of **time**, which is another basic and measurable part of the child's environment.

The home and the garden themselves, quite apart from the activities which take place in them, abound in examples of use to children in learning quite difficult mathematical ideas. The 'map' of the furniture in the living room can lead to maps of countries. The shapes of leaves can lead to discussions on what it means to say that one leaf is larger than another − heavier, of greater perimeter, of greater area, thicker, and so on.

Again, at first, one must proceed slowly. Children will certainly come to school with experience of everyday activities in which they have explored their world with their senses. They will, for example, have seen **too much** water in their baths or sometimes **too little** food on their plates. They will have called some kitchen stools **big**, others **small**. They may have heard what they would consider big being called small by an adult. The first aim must be to help children realise that such words describe **relative** size, quantity or proportion. From this realisation they must move on to understand that widely varying shapes can hold the same quantity. By pouring a given amount of sand first into one container and then into another of a different shape, a child can discover that the two containers hold the same amount of sand. Yet he may not understand what is meant when he is told that the two containers have the same **volume**: at one stage of his development the child may appear unwilling to accept the fact that a very tall thin container and a very short fat one can have the same volume. Only after sufficient experience with containers and liquids will the child come to recognise all that is meant by the phrase 'the **volume** of a container'.

Model making in Plasticine or wood will lead to further understanding of the properties of continuous 'solid' materials. The many ideas to be explored can be seen by considering the words one has to use and come to understand. The vocabulary needed includes words such as **up, down, across, on top of, in front of, behind, left, right,** as well as **hard, soft, smooth, rough,** and so on. In needlework and pattern-making we also have an obvious opportunity to include such words as **diagonal, alternate, parallel.** In constructional work, the ways in which shapes fit together must also be explored, and words such as **length, area, surface, flat, straight, round, curved, corner,** will arise naturally and be all the more acceptable later.

With an increased vocabulary and both creative and imitative experience, children can move on to learn about simple measuring processes. They may come to school using the familiar adult words such as **pints, gallons, pounds, ounces, feet** or **inches.** But these adult units are only names to children until they have had sufficient experience with their own units, such as a school milk bottle-full, a set of pebbles as weights, or a length of ribbon as a unit of length. As adults we have had continual practical experience of a pint measure, a one pound weight, or a foot rule. The child has not had this experience and must be given the opportunity to gain an understanding of the need for these standardised units of measurement before he works with them.

Work on **weight** may start with work on how many pebbles of roughly the same size balance a piece of Plasticine. Work on **length** involves experiments to find out how many given lengths of string are needed to measure the length of a classroom wall. Work on **area** must start with an examination of such questions as how many match-boxes cover a suitable table top. Later, children will want to use standardised units as a result of their work with their own units, but these adult units are unnecessary in children's preliminary investigations of their environment. Real mathematical understanding can be gained using home-made measuring instruments which are directly within the experience of the children. The very roughness of such instruments can be turned to good advantage.

Children must learn the approximate nature of **all** measurements. An accurate arithmetical calculation, $6 \times 4 = 24$, is a part of estimating the length of a table which is four lengths of a 'six-inch ribbon' long. The table is still only **approximately** twenty-four inches long, however accurate the multiplication sum. With home-made instruments children are not misled into believing in false accuracy. They can learn to estimate a measurement as **more than** six of their units but **less than** seven units, and in consequence come to a better understanding of the nature of practical measurement.

The experience gained in their work in environmental mathematics leads children into the beginnings of more purely geometical work in the third phase of development. We must recognise that children do not come to school with a ready-made geometrical frame of reference in which to set the world. **Up, down, horizontal, vertical,** are words whose pure geometrical meaning is not obvious to them. Work with plumb-lines or spirit-levels is taken for granted by adults who are used to seeing the world in a vertical-horizontal frame. Children do not see the world in this frame until they have developed the concepts involved from their own experience. Look for yourself at their drawings: walls need not be vertical to stay up, objects placed on table tops which are not horizontal do not necessarily tend to slide off the tables. Only slowly do children come to recognise the property required of a wall if it is not to tend to fall down, or of a table if the toys on it are not to tend to slide off. When such recognition has come, they can be led to grasp the fact that plumb-lines always fall **true** and that the surface of water in a bottle always stays **horizontal** whatever the position of the bottle. Recognition and understanding of these facts can only come after experience of many situations involving the relevant ideas. When they do come, one begins to see that the men standing on hillsides in the children's drawings are all standing roughly 'vertically', and not haphazardly, in relation to the frame of the picture. Out of their experience of rough practical approximations to horizontal and vertical lines, the children have abstracted pure geometrical concepts.

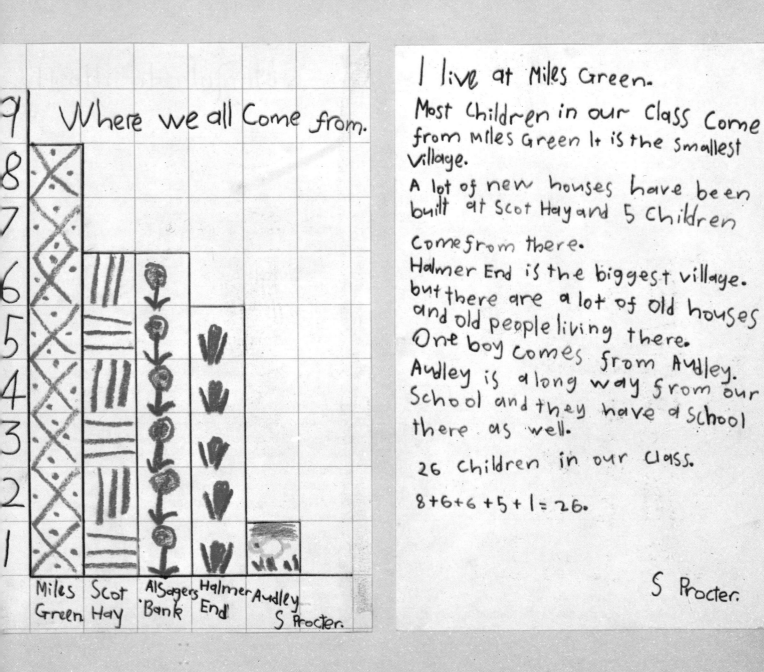

Where we all come from.

	Miles Green	Scot Hay	Alsagers Bank	Halmer End	Audley
9					
8	■				
7	■				
6	■	■	■		
5	■	■	■	■	
4	■	■	■	■	
3	■	■	■	■	
2	■	■	■	■	
1	■	■	■	■	■

S Procter.

I live at Miles Green.

Most children in our class come from Miles Green It is the smallest village.

A lot of new houses have been built at Scot Hay and 5 children come from there.

Halmer End is the biggest village. but there are a lot of old houses and old people living there.

One boy comes from Audley. Audley is a long way from our school and they have a school there as well.

26 children in our class.

$8+6+6+5+1=26.$

S Procter.

In a similar way, from practical work with roughly symmetrical shapes and patterns, children come to understand the elementary geometry of symmetrical figures. They see around them patterns made by bricks laid in the various practical ways used by bricklayers. They see how a floor can be covered in various ways by tiles of symmetrical shape. They can try to imitate these patterns in practice or by drawing pictures. From such experience they can come to recognise how the symmetry of a shape enables it to fit more readily with similar shapes. The study of the ways in which triangular shapes fit together in jigsaw fashion leads to an understanding of how triangles with equal sides are more symmetrical, and fit better together, than do triangles with unequal sides. As a result of fitting appropriate corners together, the idea of angular measurement arises naturally, not as a formal process with a manufactured protractor, but as an observation that one can subdivide a 'whole circle' into near enough equal parts by folding a paper circle for oneself. Further folding refines the process to make a more accurate measuring device.

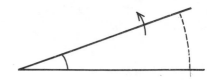

As you will see, this approach brings ideas previously treated in geometry lessons at the age of eleven or twelve to a much lower age group. Of course, to do this, the treatment of the work must change. The changes involved are made so that the basic ideas concerned are more strongly emphasised and seen in practical terms. The simple practical ideas are no longer hidden in a mass of theoretical detail imposed from outside the child's experience. One does not expect primary school children to be proving 'theorems'. One does expect them to be developing, from practical experience, an understanding of basic theoretical geometrical concepts.

Understanding how one can measure the amount a line has turned about a point is of course linked with being able to read dials: in particular, with being able to tell the time. But again we cannot immediately present children with a clock and expect them to understand time-keeping. They must have experience on which to build. Early man noticed sunsets, sunrises and variations in shadows cast by the sun and moon, long before he had clocks as such. Similarly, children are at first encouraged to be aware of the succession of events in their daily lives. Bedtime, schooltime, morning, afternoon, the successive days of the week, months of the year and birthdays are all within their experience. They can learn to refine 'amounts of time' by learning to use egg-timers, stop-watches, home-made candle 'clocks', and so on. The clock face can then be introduced gradually, first in hours, then in half hours, quarter hours, and in five-minute periods. Later, the ideas of **past** and **to** the hour can be introduced and related to the numerical way in which time is written. By slow steady progress of this kind, the concept of time, and its measurement, can be made clearer. Without an understanding of the ideas involved, the measurement is meaningless. In this respect, time is no different from any other mathematical idea involving measurement.

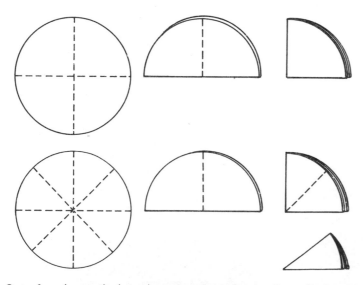

Out of such practical work comes an understanding of what is meant by the **angles of a triangle** or the **amount turned** by a line moving about a point.

Throughout all this primary work, and particularly as the children come up to the age of eight or nine and are preparing to move to middle school, emphasis is placed on the interlinking of each part of the subject with the rest. The Nuffield Project does not intend to replace the compartments **Arithmetic, Geometry** and **Mensuration** by compartments labelled **Computation, Pictorial Representation, Shape and Size**. All these are woven together: none can stand separately. The aim is to teach children to see mathematics as a unified way of thinking about the world in which they live, not as a separate collection of technical subjects.

Consider a few of the inter-relationships one can find. Links between any one measurement and the appropriate arithmetical calculations are obvious. Less obvious perhaps are the links between all such arithmetical calculations. In adding yards and feet, one must remember the number 3 (3 feet, 1 yard); in adding shillings and pence – until a few years hence, at any rate – the number 12 is vital (12 pence, 1 shilling); in ordinary arithmetic the number 10 is basic; 'on the clock' one may need 60, or 12, or 24. One can continue almost indefinitely. There is a pattern to be recognised here. The **scale of ten** in ordinary arithmetic can be replaced by any other scale one wishes. Numbers are then given different **names**, though, of course, they remain the same **numbers**. One can 'count' just as easily and effectively with the different names:

	one	two	three	four	five	six	seven
scale of 10	1	2	3	4	5	6	7
scale of 5	1	2	3	4	10	11	12
scale of 3	1	2	10	11	12	20	21
scale of 2	1	10	11	100	101	110	111

The variety of notation used here arises just as naturally as the variety in sums connected with measurement. Thus in the scale of 5, six = 1 'five' + 1 'unit', so we write six as 11 in the scale of 5. Similarly, in the scale of 2, six = 1 'four' + 1 'two' + 0 'units', so in the scale of 2, six is written 110 and read 'one, one, zero'. The 'powers' of 2, i.e. 2, 4, 8, 16, etc., take the place of the powers of 10, i.e. 10, 100, 1000, etc., in the more familiar scale of 10.

Again, one recognises the need for numbers to describe how many sides a geometrical figure has. But one can go much further and see many numerical patterns in geometrically symmetrical figures:

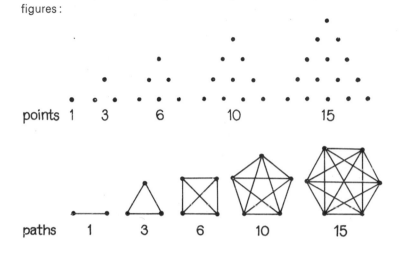

Does the pattern continue? If so, why?

In three dimensions we can ask of our solid shapes how many 'sides' or 'faces' they have and how many 'edges' and 'corners'.

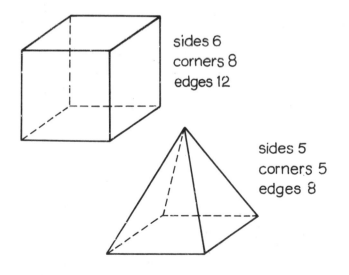

sides 6
corners 8
edges 12

sides 5
corners 5
edges 8

In both cases, 'sides' + 'corners' exceeds 'edges' by 2. Is this always true?

These links are not haphazard; there is a pattern to be discovered in each case. There are many other similar patterns which can be discovered by children, leading them to view the subject as a whole rather than in separate parts. Of course, in one child there may be a natural inclination towards the geometrical pattern rather than the numerical one; and the opposite in another. However, both can recognise the existence of each pattern and find arithmetic and geometry interlinked as they should be.

In practical as well as theoretical work, children can see unifying patterns. Thus, in measuring, **length** requires a measuring rod and a suitable unit of length. Similarly, **area** requires a suitable measuring device, say a square subdivided into suitable units; measurement of area is done then, not by way of 'length times breadth', but by application of the measuring square and by counting unit squares and parts of unit squares. **Weighing** requires a balance, and suitably subdivided units of weight. **Time** requires a clock with an associated unit of time. All measurements are approximate; their accuracy will depend on the refinements obtainable from the chosen basic units.

This chapter started with a brief look at children in relation to their parents and adult friends in the pre-school age. Your interest in their small world at that stage was asked for. Again you are asked to recognise how your child's mathematical ideas must continue to come from experience after school work has started. No teacher wants you to take over her job. But this is not to say that home and school can be separated in the child's experience. The plumb-line which falls true on the wall when father is wall-papering, the shopping basket full of pounds of this, half pounds of that, and quarter pounds of the other thing, are all as much a part of a child's experience as is work at school. If, for example, you yourself see the common pattern in weighing flour, or measuring cloth, or measuring time, both from the practical 'measuring' point of view and the purely arithmetical point of view, you can help. If you recognise the geometrical symmetry of a leaf or a building or a carpet pattern, your sympathy and interest in your child's experiences will help you to try to see the world as your child is beginning to see it. Guidance and stimulus are needed, not automatic and unthinking correction of errors in which one too often tends to assume that the child should 'see' the rightness of a 'sum' presented in adult terms, without experience of his own to back up the appropriate abstraction.

We do not ask you to teach. We ask you to try to recognise how a child develops and to use your own understanding, which has come from your own development, to help the child to take a right and proper interest, from all points of view, including a mathematical one, in his interpretation of what he sees. Above all else your interest should aim to increase your child's enjoyment of his world. There is an adventure to be found in his discoveries and development. There is fun to be gained from new experiences and 'seeing how things work'. One should add to the sense of wonderment which exists in every primary school child, and not detract from it. The teacher who avoids giving children dull repetitive tasks has to work far harder with them. She needs your support and interest to help your child meet her half-way in the work and guidance she has to offer.

An early drawing of a house and garden. Notice the lack of a precise vertical-horizontal frame, but on the other hand notice the strong sense of symmetry.

The Middle Years
Middle school work : nine to thirteen years old

No clear-cut line can be drawn between the end of primary school for children from five to nine years, and the start of middle school work for children from nine to thirteen. Individual children develop at different speeds and in different ways. One child starting middle school will, for example, see many links between different parts of mathematical work and will already be developing an understanding of the general pattern of ideas in the subject before he leaves primary school. Another child will not have gained such an understanding by this time, and will need further opportunities to develop it in the first years of middle school work, if he is to appreciate the work to be done later.

At the start of middle school work, the teacher must therefore assess what stages of development the children have reached at primary level. This can be achieved by reconsidering some of the ideas introduced at that level. Such a reconsideration provides the bridge from one level to the next.

There is a Chinese proverb :
I hear, and I forget
I see, and I remember
I do, and I understand.

The concluding phrase of this proverb is as applicable to middle school work as to work at primary level. There must be a continuity of approach to the subject. Children will still understand best through their own experience.

The basic difference between primary and middle school work carried out in this same style will, in practice, lie in the quality of the children's experience. As they grow, their imagination develops, their total experience increases, and they gain a greater fluency in their language. In consequence, their work and discussions become deeper and more wide-ranging. Ideas explored in an elementary fashion at primary level can be reconsidered in a more advanced theoretical way and in more complicated practical situations.

Technical work on volume, weight, length, costs of materials, and so on, can thus be considered by middle school children in connection with quite ambitious constructional projects. In one school, for example, children between the ages of nine and ten-plus decided to build a duck pond for a pair of ducks acquired by the school. They had to find out how much water the ducks would need and hence what would be a suitable size for the pond. They had to decide what materials to use, and hence what proportions of cement, sand and shingle would be needed to make concrete. Should the walls be constructed of concrete or brick? If of concrete, how much shuttering would be needed to hold up the walls while the concrete was setting? Would brick walls be simpler to build? Would they be watertight? How many bricks are needed to build walls three courses high around a rectangular base measuring approximately 6 feet by 4 feet? How much concrete is needed if the base is to be between 3 inches and 4 inches thick? If 1 cwt of cement, 2 cwt of sand and 3 cwt of shingle are used to make concrete, what volume of concrete is obtained? How many hundredweight bags of cement, sand and shingle would be needed to construct the required base for the pond? What would the materials cost?

The ideas involved in a project such as this are many. Some mathematical technique is necessary if such practical situations are not to give rise to unsystematic hit-and-miss mathematics. But with experience and interest, technique is easier. The reality of the situation will help to carry the children through the necessary detailed arithmetic. If they are capable of work such as this, does it matter if they are not very good at calculating

$$123 \times 3 \text{ tons 2 qr 3 st 4 lb, or } \tfrac{4}{7} \div \tfrac{3}{17} + 4\tfrac{1}{5}?$$

In preferring the real situation, with all its practical complications, and rejecting artificially complicated and unreal calculations, surely the children are showing good judgment.

Scientific uses of mathematics can also be considered. A piece of work on **area**, done by ten-year-old children, is a good example of this. The children had been discussing with a teacher the consequences of a very cold winter. They had read, in newspapers, medical advice about the need to protect small babies from low temperatures. They had come to understand how food can be thought of as a fuel for the body and how the energy produced by this fuel is lost. From these discussions it was natural to consider heat losses from the surface of the body. The children then thought it reasonable to compare the surface area of adults with that of small babies, and to relate this to food intake. At this stage they decided **for themselves** to measure the surface area of a girl in their class by laying her on paper which had a square-inch grid printed on it. An outline of the girl was drawn on the paper. The square inches wholly inside the outline were numbered and counted. The squares lying across the outline, not wholly inside or outside, were then considered. For each such square, the proportion inside the outline was estimated and all these parts of square inches added up. By this means the children obtained an estimate of the surface area of the girl in question.

Would **you** have thought of this technique? If someone asks you to think about measuring area, do you see yourself with a rectangle in front of you and a ruler in your hands, ready to measure two adjacent sides of the rectangle in preparation for doing a multiplication sum? If you do, then ask yourself whether this means you **understand** the idea of area. Would your 'length times breadth' sum help you to think of the technique used by these children in their measurement of area? Drill in multiplication sums associated with the lengths of the sides of a rectangle certainly never led any beginner to understand the idea of area. The children whose work we have just described did not even need to have been told about such sums. In earlier work they had learnt that given, for instance, a six-inch by seven-inch rectangle, they could count 42 square inches in a square-inch grid placed over it.

For such children, the rule 'area of rectangle = length times breadth' is not imposed upon them from outside. It is an obvious arithmetical aid and is not to be confused with the measuring process itself. It simply derives from their 'seven-times table': the rectangle is composed of 6 rows, each of 7 square inches; it therefore has an area of $6 \times 7 = 42$ square inches.

The two projects just described obviously helped children to learn and practise their mathematics. They also reflected the ways in which mathematics is continually being used in real life. In the duck pond project, the children gained experience of the practical technical uses of the subject. In the surface area of the body project, they used the subject in a theoretical, scientific way. Projects applying mathematics in both these ways will add reality and incentive to children's work, especially as they grow to understand more of the adult world around them.

Care is of course needed if projects are to attract all types of child. In the projects described above, building **real** brick walls will attract the practical-minded child; calculating the cost of the bricks and cement used will hold the interest of the less practical child. The child who is always asking 'Why?' can learn something about scientific enquiry from the project on the surface area

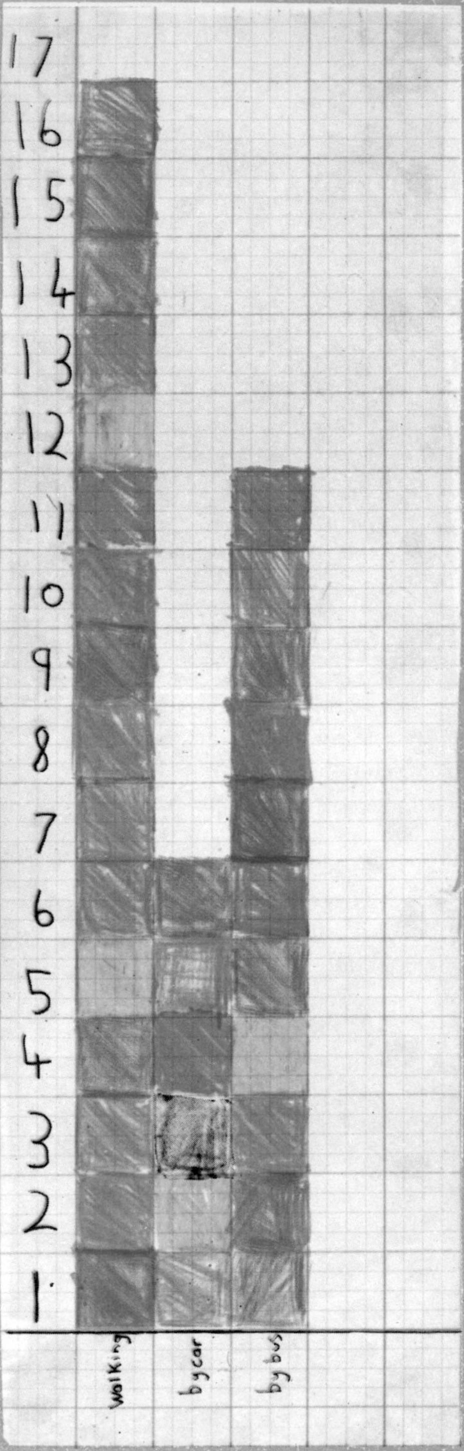
17
16
15
14
13
12
11
10
9
8
7
6
5
4
3
2
1
walking
by car
by bus

Richard 7 years.

The graph tells us that most people walk home from school. It tells you that eleven people come by bus. It tells you that 6 people come by car. It tells you that there are 33 people in the class. It tells you that 10 more people walk home than go by car. And 5 more people come by bus than by car. And it shows you that 5 more people walk home from school than go by bus

Kathleen Harrison   Age 9
Adding Square

1	2	3	4	5	6	7	8	9	10
11	12	13	14	15	16	17	18	19	20
21	22	23	24	25	26	27	28	29	30
31	32	33	34	35	36	37	38	39	40
41	42	43	44	45	46	47	48	49	50
51	52	53	54	55	56	57	58	59	60
61	62	63	64	65	66	67	68	69	70
71	72	73	74	75	76	77	78	79	80
81	82	83	84	85	86	87	88	89	90
91	92	93	94	95	96	97	98	99	100

This square is very interesting. It shows that every number which has a red ring round it is every sixth number starting from two instead of nothing. As well as that the numbers which have purple rings round them are every fourth number starting from six. Also each number that has a yellow ring round it is counting in three's starting from number four.

of the body; the arithmetical work involved in estimating the total area will attract the child with a numerical turn of mind. Like any other group of individuals, children in a middle school class will at one time or another vary from those who prefer to 'do' to those who prefer to 'think'. If each type of child is to gain from membership of a project-group, the arrangement of the groups will require professional judgment. Very few projects can or should be designed for one type of child only. Some projects will be best tackled by groups of mixed ability and interests, some by those of common ability, and some by groups of close companions. The teacher organising project work must consider a child's working speed relative to that of his fellows, the ways in which one child's type of work fits with another's, and the ways in which a child will learn from his friends. The Nuffield Introductory Guide **I do, and I understand** is designed to help teachers organising such work, and a film (with the same title) shows the kind of results which can be achieved.

An outline of mathematical work at primary level can only be given in terms of basic concepts, **number, length, area, weight,** and so on. At middle school level it is perhaps easier for the layman to distinguish **arithmetic, geometry** or **algebra.** It is therefore wise to realise that it is still **mathematics** which is being taught. In practice, there are no strict dividing lines between the various branches of the subject. There are times when an **arithmetical** approach is appropriate, rather than an **algebraic** one, or a **geometrical** one, but there is no rule or law which forbids one approach to a problem to be used in preference to another. Thus, although for convenience one may describe middle school work under the three broad headings of arithmetic, geometry and algebra, the common patterns and features of the various types of work must be emphasised. Artificial barriers should not be raised between the different branches of the subject.

Arithmetic at primary level begins with work designed to help children grasp the idea of the 'whole' numbers, 1, 2, 3 . . . . Only when this idea is well understood do we expect real success in work with the fundamental arithmetical operations of addition and multiplication. In a similar fashion, early in the middle school programme there must be arithmetical work designed to help the children begin to understand the need for numbers other than the whole numbers. The arithmetical operations of subtraction and division are not going to be thoroughly understood until children have grasped the ideas of **negative numbers** and **fractions** respectively.

The method of introducing only one of these, namely fractions, will be mentioned here. The work must of course form an extension of earlier work. Thus if the teaching of **division** at middle school level is to be linked with 'sharing-out sums' and fractions (just as the teaching of subtraction is linked with 'taking-away sums' and negative numbers), work at primary level connected with 'sharing-out sums' must be designed so that it can be extended in a natural fashion at the later stage. There should therefore not be an over-emphasis on statements such as '4 into 2 won't go' at primary level. Rather, when appropriate, children should be encouraged to see 'whole' things divided into halves, quarters, and so on, for just as they can **share out** sweets, so they can **cut up** cakes. If 2 children share 4 sweets equally between them, they get 2 sweets each. So also, if 4 children share 2 cakes equally between them, they get $\frac{1}{2}$ a cake each. 4 into 2 **does** go.

Middle school division can then start in a quite practical way with scissors and paper strip if necessary, demonstrating the simplest possible case, that of 'halving'. The child will certainly be able to 'double' and will be aware of the sequence one, two, four, eight, ... In simple arithmetical work this sequence will have been used as a 'base' for number work, so that the statement

$$7 = 1 \text{ four} + 1 \text{ two} + 1 \text{ unit}$$

will have led to 7 being represented as 111 'in the scale of two'. By halving, to obtain $\frac{1}{2}, \frac{1}{4}, \frac{1}{8}, \ldots$, the pattern appropriate to the scale of two:

eights	fours	twos	units

can thus be extended to the right:

In such a scale, for example, the number $5\frac{3}{4}$ is expressed as 101·11, since

$$5\frac{3}{4} = 1\text{ four} + 0\text{ twos} + 1\text{ unit} + 1\text{ half} + 1\text{ quarter.}$$

Other scales are just as practicable. In particular the decimal or denary scale takes its place as the one most commonly met with in ordinary life:

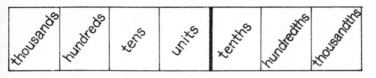

This denary scale is thus not a unique system, but one preferred method of representing numbers. Confidence in the technique of manipulating decimals is gained from the understanding of this general method of number representation.

After work on decimals or in any other scale, one can begin to learn how the rules of arithmetic are used in work with fractions. Here again there is much to be done which can make these rules appear natural, and not artificial. In the addition of fractions, for example, experience must be given which will make ·children regard the process of **bringing to a common denominator** as an obvious one. Work on different scales of notation will have given children an understanding that a number can have many different 'names'. They can prepare lists, almost ad infinitum, of the different ways in which any number can be represented, but basically they have grasped the point when they recognise that $1\frac{1}{2}$ is written 1·5 in the scale of ten, i.e. as a decimal, and 1·1 in the scale of two. Thus when they see $\frac{1}{2}$ also written $\frac{2}{4}, \frac{3}{6}, \frac{4}{8}$, and so on, they will not be meeting a fundamentally different idea. In this way, adding $\frac{1}{2}$ to $\frac{3}{4}$ can be linked with the idea that one should only add 'like to like'. Hence the calculation

$$\frac{1}{2} + \frac{3}{4} = \frac{2}{4} + \frac{3}{4} = \frac{5}{4}.$$

In doing this the children have only to observe that they should be adding **quarters** to **quarters**. They may well be helped by having seen such sums done in the following way in the scale of two:

units	halves	quarters	
	1		$= \frac{1}{2}$
	1	1	$= \frac{3}{4}$
1	0	1	$= 1\frac{1}{4}$

'Bringing to a common denominator', in this case 4, was quite simple here. In more complicated cases, as, say, in $\frac{1}{3} + \frac{1}{4}$, the children will be able to call upon the experience they have had in producing factors and in isolating **prime** numbers:

product	factors (primes)
1	(1, 1)
2	(1, **2**)
3	(1, **3**)
4	(1, **2**, 4)
5	(1, **5**)
6	(1, **2**, **3**, 6)
7	(1, **7**)

Children who have produced tables of this kind will know the required factorisation $12 = 3 \times 4$, so that they can write

$$\frac{1}{3} + \frac{1}{4} = \frac{4}{12} + \frac{3}{12} = \frac{7}{12}.$$

In this way, the children's mathematical experience first makes rules (in this case, of addition) appear reasonable and natural; secondly, it gives them confidence to use the appropriate technique in their application of the rules. Building up mathematical ability in this way is good practice at **any** level, not just in primary or middle school.

When subtraction is preceded by work on negative numbers, and division by work on fractions, one can draw out a common pattern and then compare it with other arithmetical situations. As work through middle school proceeds, this pattern can be made more evident. One may first for example observe that 0 is related to addition as 1 is related to multiplication, for 0 **added** to any number leaves that number unaltered, just as 1 **multiplied** by any number leaves that number the same:

$$0 + 3 = 3 = 3 + 0$$
$$1 \times 3 = 3 = 3 \times 1.$$

One can then observe that the negative of a number is related to 0 by way of addition in the same way as the inverse of a number is related to 1 by way of multiplication:

$$(-3) + 3 = 0 = 3 + (-3)$$
$$(\tfrac{1}{3}) \times 3 = 1 = 3 \times (\tfrac{1}{3}).$$

Subtraction is seen as 'addition of the negative'; division as 'multiplication by the inverse'.

Recognition of such patterns, linked with a use of symbols rather than numbers, gives the lead into algebra, where structure, pattern and rules of behaviour of mathematical systems are the subject of study. It is **not** the object of the Nuffield Project to give highly abstract symbolic algebraic work to middle school children, but it **is** the intention of the Project to see that they leave middle school aware of many of the algebraic patterns present in all their work.

Thus, in their arithmetic, one can lead children to see that without the negative numbers they could not solve the algebraic equation:

$$3 + x = 0.$$

Equally without fractions, they could not solve the equation:

$$3x = 1.$$

With positive, negative and fractional numbers can they solve all the equations they can write down? Can they solve the equation:

$$x^2 = 2,$$

i.e. do they know a positive, negative or fractional number which multiplied by itself gives 2? If they cannot find such a number, what about the length of the diagonal of a square whose side is 1 inch? What will Pythagoras' theorem in their geometrical work tell them about the length of this diagonal? Can they approximate by fractions, or decimals, the number whose square is 2?

There are deep and hard mathematical ideas here, but the questions can be made to arise in a reasonable and natural fashion. The fact that the answers to children's questions are hard

is surely no reason for denying them the opportunity of asking them nor avoiding discussing the problems involved if we feel we can help them by so doing.

In a different direction, the experience gained by children in primary school in doing arithmetic on a clock can be turned to good account in seeing structure in their work. They will readily accept the idea of constructing a clock on which the usual twelve hours are replaced by 5, and 'midnight' or 'noon' is regarded as 0.

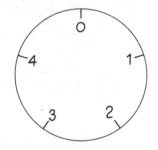

They will follow then the usual procedure in clock arithmetic: in all addition sums 'forget' multiples of 5, unless one is interested in the number of 'days' involved in the sum, which we are not. Thus they can construct their addition table for the arithmetic of the 5-clock:

+	O	1	2	3	4
O	O	1	2	3	4
1	1	2	3	4	O
2	2	3	4	O	1
3	3	4	O	1	2
4	4	O	1	2	3

The calculations involved here are easy and give good practice in simple arithmetic. Thus, for example, 'forgetting' 5's, **4 + 3 = 2**, since 4 + 3 = 2 + 5, or again **4 + 4 = 3**, since 4 + 4 = 8 = 3 + 5.

Gary (aged 6) has sorted out the things he needed to make his rocket.

This is a rocker The men go up the stairs in to the rocker

wooden round pole

Gory
Tyde

corner

brass ring

square
with
hole

Srick

glass pot

up side
down

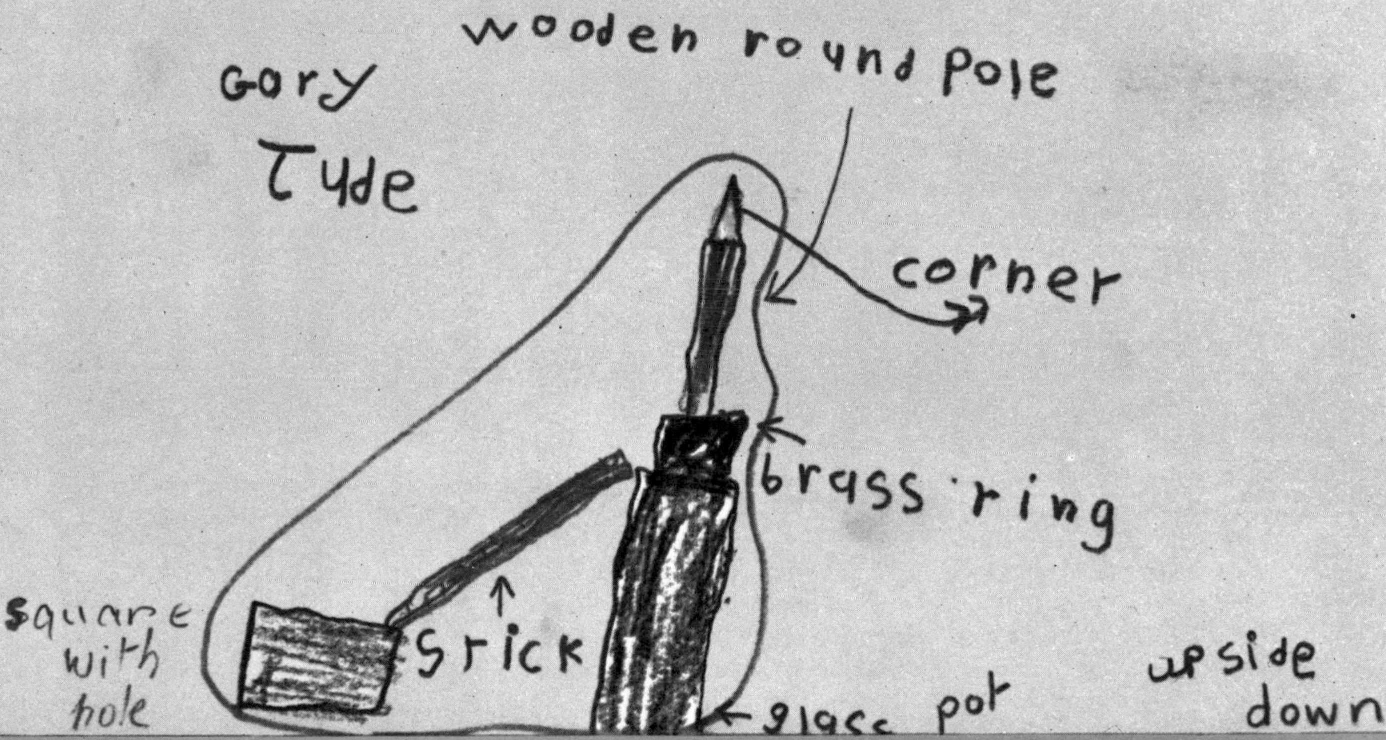

Work in clock arithmetic can be seen as a natural extension of ordinary arithmetic. It is most important however to notice that on the clock '+' and '×' are not the ordinary arithmetical '+' and '×'. Might one therefore expect to find other mathematical situations in which the symbols '+' and '×' could be used algebraically? If so, how would you recognise that it was reasonable to use them?

At this stage, the basic rules of addition and multiplication, expressed in algebraic form, must be recognised:

$$a + b = b + a$$
$$a \times b = b \times a$$
$$a + (b + c) = (a + b) + c$$
$$a \times (b \times c) = (a \times b) \times c$$
$$0 + a = a$$
$$1 \times a = a$$

and so on. If these rules are to be recognised in this form, children must gain experience of other concrete mathematical situations where the rules apply. The **algebra** of the modern syllabus at late middle school and at secondary level is the study of mathematical systems, and their rules, expressed in symbolic form. The arithmetic of the number line and of the clock are but a part of the work, and at middle school level the children must gain experience of other situations in which algebraic methods are appropriate. **Number work done symbolically is not sufficient,** either for appreciating modern attitudes towards the theoretical operations of mathematics, or for understanding modern practical uses of the subject.

Thus geometrical work at middle school level must be linked with this algebraic attitude, and primary work on patterns and symmetry must be designed so that development in this direction is possible. In fact the instructions one uses at primary level — **fold** this, **move** that, **turn over** that piece, **rotate** through that angle — are all capable of symbolic representation. The extension of primary work on practical symmetry into a more theoretical study of the geometry of the world in which we live, can easily carry with it the appropriate algebraic work.

Consider for example the rotations of a triangle ABC, with equal sides, about a centre 0:

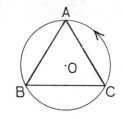

Let us restrict our attention to rotations in which we change positions as follows:

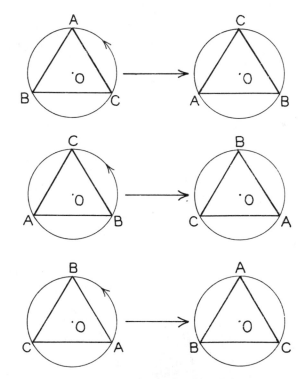

To obtain these illustrations we gave the instruction 'rotate the triangle through 120°, in each case. If one writes this instruction 'R', we would be asking the illustrator to draw the change:

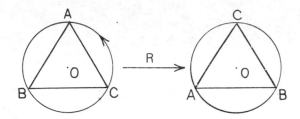

If we wrote 'RR', he would draw:

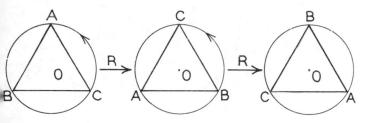

If one then gives the instruction 'RRR', one gets:

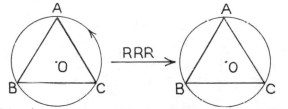

We finish where we started! In fact the instruction RRR produces the same effect as multiplication by 1 in ordinary arithmetic. We can associate with this geometrical situation a simple table, like an arithmetical table:

	I	R	RR
I	I	R	RR
R	R	RR	I
R	RR	I	R

Here the entry in a given row and column is obtained by giving the instruction for the row and then the instruction for the column and entering in the table the appropriate symbol I, R, or RR, where I means 'make no change'. Thus

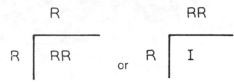

since RRR produces the same effect as I.

Now compare this table with the 3-clock addition table:

+	0	1	2
0	0	1	2
1	1	2	0
2	2	0	1

If we write 0 for I, 1 for R, 2 for RR, the one table becomes the other. The 'algebra' of rotations of an equilateral triangle through 120° is the same as the algebra of addition on the 3-clock.

All such situations of an 'instructional' type are capable of a similar analysis, and offer work in abundance for middle school children. Here they can gain familiarity with a more theoretical aspect of the geometrical work they have done at primary level. Of course this must be linked with non-symbolic work on the geometry of figures. But this presents no problems, for the traditional geometry of triangles, circles, and so on, can be readily given in terms of the 'movements' one associates with practical geometrical work. In such work one turns figures, i.e. **rotates** them; one sees figures in a mirror, i.e. **reflects** them; one moves figures without turning them, i.e. **translates** them. Thus, a simple fact of geometry, that the angles at the base of an isosceles triangle are equal (see over)

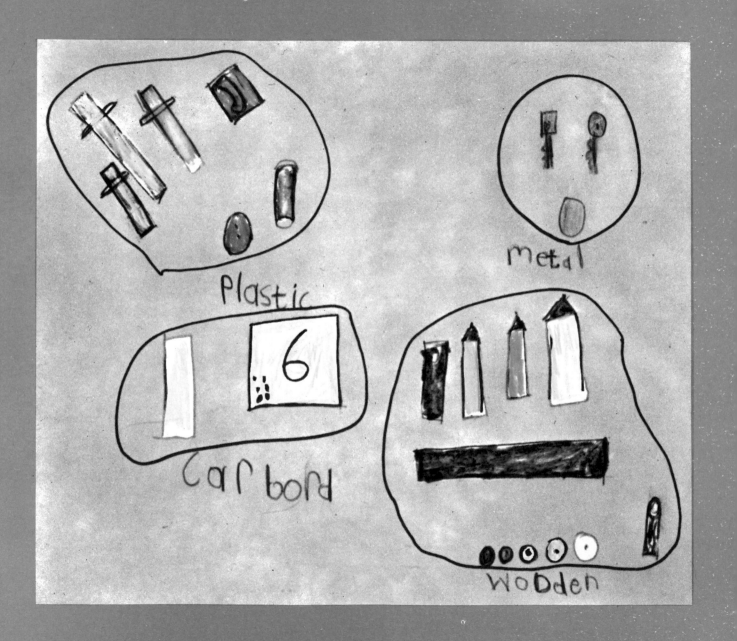

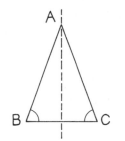

can easily be **seen** to be true by folding the triangle along the dotted line so that the angles B and C coincide. Such a folding process can be made to yield a **proof** when theoretical 'motion' geometry is taught later. This geometry is then the study of the theory of rotations, reflections and translations. It fits more easily than does traditional geometry with one's natural inclination to verify that geometrical figures are 'equal' by bringing them into coincidence.

Another example which may be more familiar is a proof of Pythagoras' theorem, that the square on the hypotenuse of a right-angled triangle is equal to the sum of the squares on the two other sides :

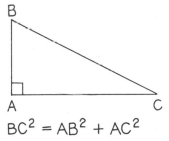

$$BC^2 = AB^2 + AC^2$$

Here one draws squares, cuts along appropriate lines and finds that the geometrical squares do fit together in an appropriate fashion. One has to translate and rotate and cut up, but none of those operations will affect the areas involved :

Charles (aged 6) eventually partitioned his set of objects into four sub-sets : 'plastic', 'metal', 'cardboard', 'wooden'. Note that every element in Charles' set was clearly distinguishable by him.

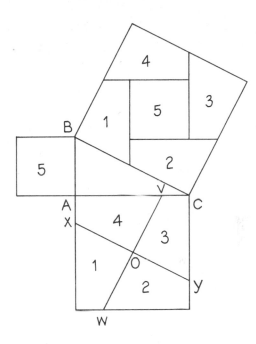

Again, operations which can actually be carried out can be used as a basis for eventual theoretical proof.

This marriage of practical geometrical work with theoretical work through the theoretical interpretation of turning, moving, reflecting, and so on, can prove to be one of the most attractive parts of middle school work. The practical work can continue from primary school, but the theoretical aspect is always in view on the horizon. When treated symbolically it extends the range of the mathematical work in a way which few other topics can. Project-work for the practical-minded, and for the more theoretical-minded, can be found throughout the work. The fact that the practical-minded child is at first more convinced of the truth of Pythagoras' theorem, say, by a physical verification which he makes himself, than by a highly theoretical logical proof, is no reflection of the child's lack of mathematical understanding. If he wishes to proceed to higher mathematics there will be ample opportunity to introduce him to formal logical arguments. At middle school the child must get some guidance towards the mathematical questions to be asked later in his school life. Questions raised by the exploration of mathematics in relation to the world around him will arise naturally if they come from his own experience. If he **convinces** himself of correct answers, without necessarily at first being able to **prove** the correctness of these answers, middle school teaching in the subject will have succeeded, not failed.

We emphasised the need to recognise, in primary work, the usefulness of geometrical representations of mathematical information, particularly in graphical form. To emphasise once again that middle school mathematics as we have described it is not conceived of as a purely theoretical classroom study, we may finally note that much graphical work can be linked at this level with the collection and simple interpretation of statistics. Consider statements such as:

More men than women wear glasses.
All the people in the village want an hourly bus service.
Chloro washes whiter.

Children at this stage will certainly meet such statements in their everyday lives. Are they verifiable? Can we obtain numerical information to verify them? How would school work of this kind differ from work carried out by commercial groups doing statistical work for advertisement purposes?

Such questions can lead to the teacher-class discussion which is a basic ingredient of the modern teaching programme. Graphs from newspapers can be brought to school. Children's opinions on topics of interest to them can be canvassed. Class absences can be displayed graphically. Even gambling fallacies can be explored — coins tossed, dice thrown, cards picked from packs of cards. This is how the mathematical theory of probability grew in the first place, and the experiences which led mathematicians to develop their theories in the subject can easily be made available in the classroom. We live in an age of numerical data and only by early experience of it in organised form will children come to recognise the need for statistical analysis of such data, and the strengths and weaknesses of statistical claims.

We come, as it were, full circle in all our work. From our experience we enter mathematics, from our mathematical thinking we re-enter the practical world around us. In this respect, the adult stands within a wider circle than does the child. The modern programme to which your child will be exposed will certainly ensure that his circle is not **wholly** within your own.

We leave you in the hands of your children. They may well lead you to see and hear new ideas — the scope of their work at primary and middle school level can be described only briefly in a short guide such as this. Your interest and stimulus will be best appreciated if they come from a desire to know more for yourself. Any teacher will tell you how much can be learned about a subject through trying to teach it. When your child tries to tell you about his work at school, he is learning for himself. Your desire to know and understand can thus be a stimulus to your child in his learning. Experiences at home and school are complementary. Your interest, at home, in your child's education can only be an influence for good in his work at school.

The first publications of the Nuffield Mathematics Project include

Introductory Guide

I do, and I understand ●■▼

This guide explains the intentions of the Project, gives detailed descriptions of the ways in which a changeover from conventional teaching can be made and faces many of the problems that will be met.

Teachers' Guides

Pictorial Representation 1

Designed to help teachers of children between the ages of 5 and 10, this guide deals with graphical representation in its many aspects.

Beginnings ▼

This guide deals with the early awareness of both the meaning of number and the relationships which can emerge from everyday experiences of measuring length, capacity, area, time, etc.

Mathematics Begins ●

A parallel guide to *Beginnings* ▼ , but more concerned with 'counting numbers' than with measurement. It contains a considerable amount of background information for the teacher.

Shape and Size ▼²

The first Guide concerned principally with geometrical ideas. It shows how geometrical concepts can be developed from the play stage in *Beginnings* ▼ to a clearer idea of what volume, area, horizontal and symmetrical really mean.

Computation and Structure ❷

Here the concept of number is further developed. A section on the history of natural numbers and weights and measures leads on to the operation of addition, place value, different number bases, odd and even numbers, the application of number strips and number squares.

Shape and Size ▼³

Continues the geometrical work of ▼² . Examination of two-dimensional shapes leads on to angles, symmetry and patterns, and links up with the more arithmetical work of ❷ .

Computation and Structure ❸

Suggests an abundance of ways of introducing children to multiplication so that they will understand what they are doing rather than simply follow rules.

Weaving Guides

Desk Calculators

Points out a number of ways in which calculators can be used constructively in teaching children number patterns, place value and multiplication and division in terms of repeated addition and subtraction.

How to Build a Pond

A facsimile reproduction of a class project.